ADVENTURE TIME™
Created by **PENDLETON WARD**

"RICARDIO ARRYTHMIA"
Written & Illustrated by
AARON MCCONNELL

"MASTERS OF THE
POWERSKULL SWORD"
Written & Illustrated by
BENJAMIN MARRA
Colors by
ALEKSANDR GUSHKY

"GLADIATOR REALM"
Written & Illustrated by
JAMIE COE

"FAVORITE SHIRT"
Written & Illustrated by
REZA FARAZMAND

"SWORD OF THE SUN"
Written & Illustrated by
CARISSA POWELL

"BILLY THE HERO"
Written by
BRANDON ZUERN
Illustrated by
MATT FRANK
Colors by
GONÇALO LOPES
Letters by
MIKE FIORENTINO

"FOREVER (NOT) ALONE"
Written & Illustrated by
XIAO TONG KONG

"KEY TO THE BREAKFAST
KINGDOM"
Written & Illustrated by
JACK SJOGREN

"PICKLING WITH PRISMO"
Written & Illustrated by
JEAN WEI

"THE ARCADE"
Written & Illustrated by
MARI ARAKAKI

"MIGHTIER THAN THE FIST"
Written & Illustrated by
BEN PASSMORE

"BANDITOS"
Written by
TYLER JENKINS
Illustrated by
BOYA SUN
Letters by
WARREN MONTGOMERY

"CANDY FINN"
Written & Illustrated by
MORGAN BEEM

"BUS STOP"
Written & Illustrated by
SONNY LIEW

Cover by
RICHARD CHANG

Series Designer
GRACE PARK

Collection Designer
KARA LEOPARD

Assistant Editors
**MICHAEL MOCCIO
KATALINA HOLLAND**

Editor
WHITNEY LEOPARD

With Special Thanks to Marisa Marionakis, Janet No, Curtis Lelash, Conrad
Montgomery, Kelly Crews, Scott Malchus, Adam Muto and the wonderful
folks at Cartoon Network.

OOO...

IT'S EITHER HEART-ACHE OR TERRIBLE HORRENDOUS GLOB-AWFUL INDIGESTION.

GUNTER, I NEED YOU TO MUSTER ALL YOU BIRDY BRAIN JUI AND HELP ME FIN A WAY TO EASE THIS SUFFERIN

CAN YOU DO THAT FOR ME, SWEETIE?

I'LL JUST ASSUME THAT YOU'LL PONDER IT DEEPLY AND GET BACK TO ME...

OH SWEET DISTRACTION!

WELCOME BACK TO THE ROYAL PUDDING BAKE-OFF AND WRESTLING COMPETITION, THE MOST ANTICIPATED TELEVISED EVENT OF THE YEAR!

OH GOODY!

WE'RE ABOUT TO MEET THE CONTESTANTS, PRINCESSES FROM ACROSS THE LAND OF OOO WHO PREPARE THE PUDDING THAT THEY THEMSELVES WILL BE WRESTLING IN!

OH MERCY! NOT EVEN MY FAVORITE SHOW CAN -OW!- DISTRACT ME FROM THIS -UNG!- DISCOMFORT!

BREAKFAST PRINCESS, TELL US ABOUT THE BREAD PUDDING THAT WILL BE THE BASE FOR YOUR MATCH AGAINST WILDBERRY PRINCESS...

FWOOSH!

WHAT ARE YOU DOING TO ME, RICARDIO? I CAN'T LIVE LIKE THIS!

THAT'S FOR SURE! YOU CAN'T LIVE LIKE THIS, SITTING AROUND WATCHING SHOWS WHEN YOU NEED TO BE OUT THERE MEETING PRINCESSES!

I'VE HAD TO TAKE MATTERS INTO MY OWN HANDS!!

I DON'T WANT TO GET TOO TECHNICAL WITH YOU, BUT LET ME PUT IT THIS WAY...

I'VE BEEN TURNING YOUR INSIDES INTO A GO-CART TRACK AND TELLING ALL THE TEENY BLOODCELL BOPPERS THAT IT'S RACING SEASON. THE PRESSURE'S ON AND IT'S GOING TO STAY THAT WAY UNTIL WE MAKE AN ARRANGEMENT.

YOU BRING A WHOLE NEW MEANING TO A HEART ATTACK, RICARDIO. TELL ME, HOW DO YOU EXPECT TO ROMANCE PRINCESSES WITH ME HUNCHED OVER MY GUTS AND SWEATING BULLETS?

BAH! I'D BE BETTER OFF WITHOUT YOU, BELIEVE ME!!

3

UM, WHY DON'T YOU GO FIRST?

I WILL! I WISH TO BE FREE OF THE ICE KING ONCE AND FOR ALL!

OW! THAT STINGS!

OKAY, MY TURN... HERE WE GO... UM... I, THE ICE KING, WOULD LIKE RICARDIO, MY HEART, TO GO AWAY AND BE SOME OTHER CREATURE'S HEART SO I DON'T HAVE TO DEAL WITH HIS SELFISH DESIRES.

UH, HOLD IT! I NEED TO CHANGE MY WISH! IT NEEDS TO BE MORE SPECIFIC!

SORRY, NO DO-OVERS! THE DEMONIC WISHING EYE WILL NOW GRANT YOUR WISHES!

CLAP!

OH BOY! PEE-EW! WISH FULFILLMENT SURE HAS A PUNGENT ODOR, DOESN'T IT, GUNTER?

BUT HEY! YOU KNOW WHAT? I FEEL DIFFERENT!

I FEEL LIGHTER, AS IF A GREAT BURDEN HAS LIFTED AWAY!

HELLO-O-O! YOU AREN'T IN THERE ARE YOU, RICARDIO?

TUNKA TUNKA

HEH HEH, THAT MELON IS RIPE! GIVE IT A THUMP THERE, GUNTER!

"EMPTY AS A POCKET WITH NOTHING TO LOSE!"

TA-NA-NA!

SLAP

5

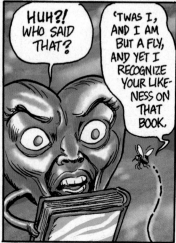

MEANWHILE, BACK IN THE ICE KINGDOM...

WAH-HOO!

HA HA HA! LIGHT AS A FEATHER!

AH GUNTER, IT FEELS GOOD TO BE UNFETTERED DOESN'T IT? THAT USUAL YEARNING IS GONE, AND I HAVEN'T PINED FOR A PRINCESS SINCE RICARDIO LEFT.

IN FACT I'M PERFECTLY CONTENT TO SIMPLY PASS THE TIME WATCHING CLOUDS DRIFT BY...

YOU'RE RIGHT, IT'S PROBABL TIME TO EAT SOME FOOD OF SOMETHING.

WELL, NOTHING IN THE ICE BOX IS REALLY CALLING OUT TO ME, MAYBE I'M NOT THAT HUNGRY.

MIGHT AS WELL GO FOR SOME ICE CREAM, THAT'S ALWAYS BEEN A FAVORITE. YOU WANT SOME ICE CREAM, GUNTER!

BON APPÉTIT, MY SWEETIE! HERE'S TO THE GOOD LIFE!

HMM...

STRANGE.... I'M NOT GETTING THE USUAL LIFT WHEN IT HITS THE TONGUE. DOES THIS ICE CREAM TASTE A LITTLE HO-HUM TO YOU, GUNTER?

SLURP GLORP SLURP!

NO, APPARENTLY NOT.

UGH, IF I HAVE TO SUCK THE BACKWASH OUT OF ONE MORE EMPTY JUICE BOX, I SWEAR I'LL END IT ALL.

SPEAK NOT IN THIS WAY, BRAVE HEART.

HUH?

OH, IT'S YOU. HOW'S THE GOOD LIFE?

IT HAS BEEN A GOOD LIFE, WHEN LAST WE SPOKE I WAS BUT YOUNG AND SPRY, NOW I'VE GROWN OLD AND WILL SOON DIE.

DIE?! IT'S ONLY BEEN A FEW DAYS!

DAYS TO YOU HAVE BEEN A LIFETIME TO ME. I'VE TRAVELLED THE VALLEYS & CORRIDORS OF THIS VESSEL. MY JOURNEY BROUGHT ME FLY TO FLY WITH LOVE AND LIFE, WHEREBY I LEARNED TO TEACH & TAUGHT TO LEARN, BUT NOW I GROW WEARY AND MUST TAKE MY REST.

BUT WAIT! YOU MUST TELL ME-- WHAT IS THIS PLACE? IS THERE ANY WAY OUT?

TRUE LOVE WILL FIND YOU IN THE END.

THE END?

NO, MY MISTAKE, SORRY... THE OTHER PART...

THE OTHER PART?! COME ON, OLD FLY, STAY WITH ME! WHAT ARE YOU TALKING ABOUT?

I'M SORRY ... I AM BUT A FLY.

YOU'LL ALWAYS BE A BUTTERFLY TO ME.

GOODBYE, MY FRIEND.

WONDER WHAT IT MEANS, TRUE LOVE WILL FIND YOU NOT IN THE END, BUT THE OTHER PART? ... THE BEGINNING? THE FRONT?

THE ONLY DISTINGUISHABLE FEATURE IN THIS PLACE IS THIS SEEMINGLY IMPENETRABLE RABBIT HOLE.

☼ SIGH ☼

I CAN'T BELIEVE I FEEL HOMESICK FOR THE COLD EMBRACE OF THE ICE KING'S CHEST CAVITY. LOOKS LIKE I'VE BEEN DUPED.

?

17

The End

aamcconnell 2018

MASTERS OF THE POWERSKULL SWORD

THIS DUNGEON GOES ON **FOREVER**!

I CAN'T BELIEVE WE DEFEATED A WHOLE **HIVE** OF FLYING MIND WORMS!

I THINK THIS IS THE **LAST** ROOM THOUGH!

YEAH, DUDE, AND THOSE GIANT FRUIT BATS WITH THOSE **FACES** BLECH!

WE DESERVE WHATEVER TREASURE IS IN THIS ROOM! IT LOOKS **EMPTY**!

NAH, DUDE! CHECK OUT THAT **SWORD**!

WRITTEN & DRAWN BY BENJAMIN MARRA

COLORS BY ALEKSANDR GRUSHKY

AWESOME! IT **GLOWS**!

I BET IT'S WORTH A LOT OF **GOLD**!

I DON'T KNOW, MAN! I GOT A **BAD** FEELING!

MY HACKLES ARE HACKLING!

IT'S GOTTA BE **MAGIC**! LIKE, +1 TO HIT AT LEAST!

TINK!

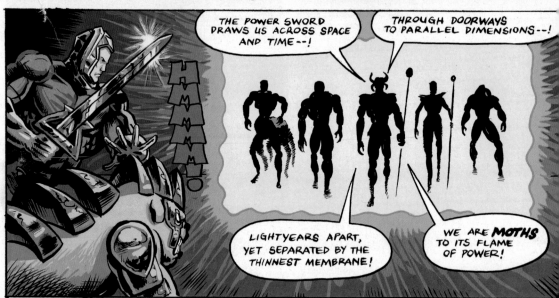

THE END?

GLADIATOR REALM

JAMIE COE

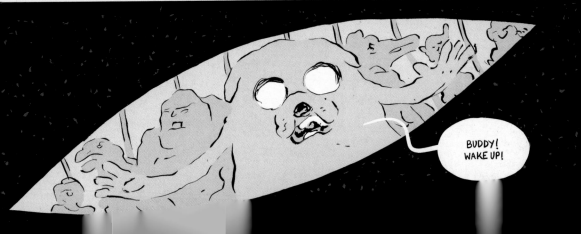

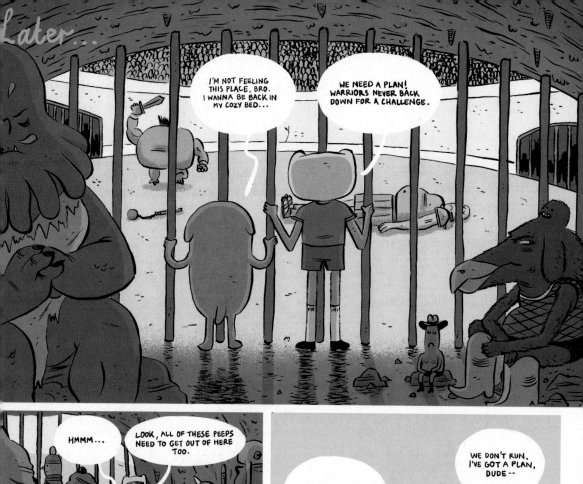

I'M NOT FEELING THIS PLACE, BRO. I WANNA BE BACK IN MY COZY BED...

WE NEED A PLAN! WARRIORS NEVER BACK DOWN FOR A CHALLENGE.

HMMM...

LOOK, ALL OF THESE PEEPS NEED TO GET OUT OF HERE TOO.

WE COULD DIG A HOLE? OR... WE COULD RUN?

WE DON'T RUN. I'VE GOT A PLAN, DUDE --

--AND IT INVOLVES ALL OF US.

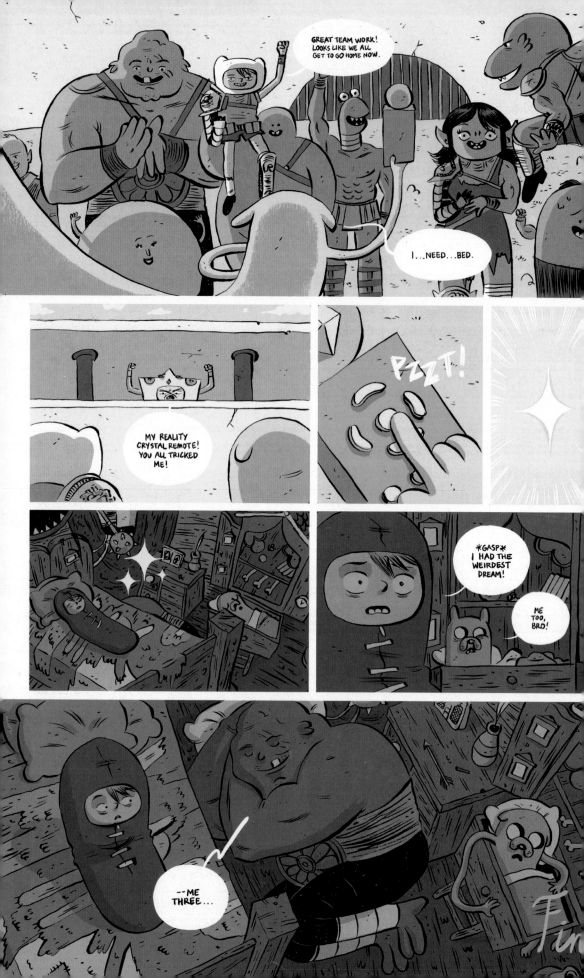

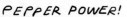

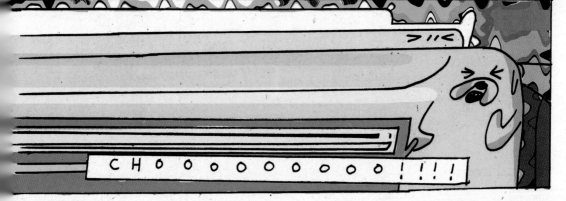

BEEEEE MOOOOO!

I FEEL WEIRD, MAN!

HOW LONG ARE WE GONNA DRIFT BACKWARDS?

FOREVER!

NOW GOOD TIMES WILL NEVER END!

OH NO, MAN — I CAN FEEL MY PUPPY FUR GROWING!

SO HOW DO WE GET BACK???

WE CAN SNEEZE OUR WAY BACK!

SNEEZE?!!

SNEEZING IS THE ONLY WAY TO REVERSE TIME'S DIRECTION!

YOU BET!

I GET IT... FINN! YOU STILL GOT THAT PEPPER SHAKER?

HANG ON TIGHT, DUDES!

SNIFF

AH... AH...

CHOO

OOF!

OOF

OW!

WHAM BAM PEPPER SLAM!

UGH

SNOT IS GROSS.

END!

SWORD OF THE SUN
WRITTEN & ILLUSTRATED BY CARISSA KAYE POWELL

What can you never eat for breakfast?

Dinner!

Good enough.

THE EN

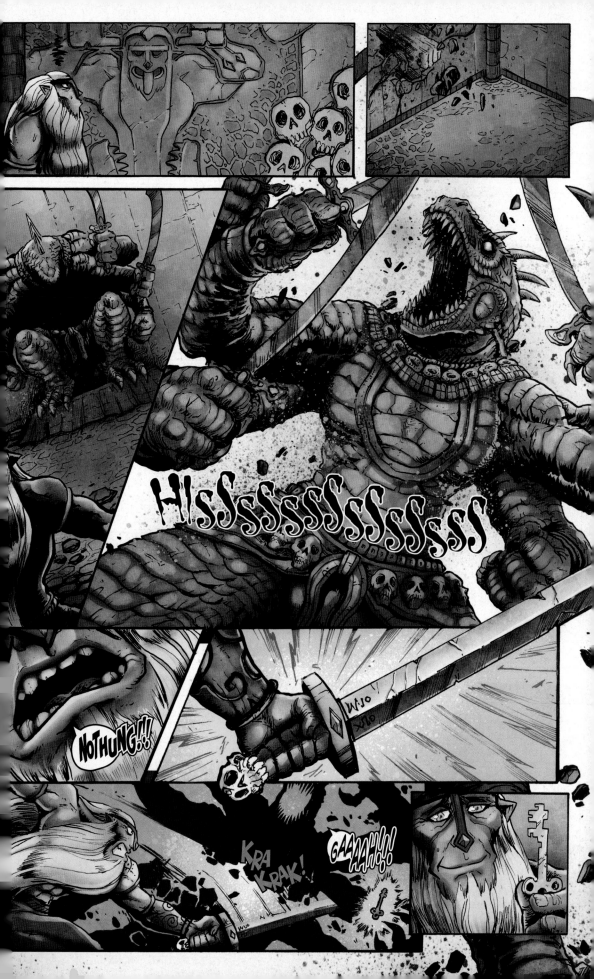

That was his story. Billy, the fool.

WHATEVS!
I GOTTA RUN
SOME ERRANDS.

MAKE SURE NOTHIN'
GOES DOWN WHEN
I'M OUT.

YES, MA'AM!

PLEASE DON'T CALL
ME THAT.

YES, PERSON!

SO HOW MUCH
OF A KEY...

IS THIS
KEY?

IT'S
SYMBOLIC.

IT'S NOT
A REAL KEY,
DUDE.

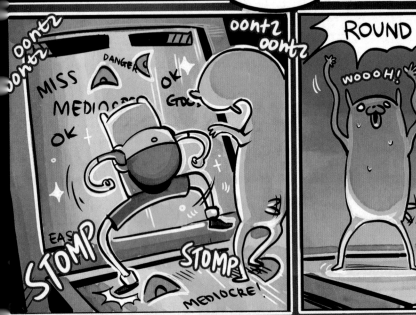

THANK YOU FOR PLAYING!

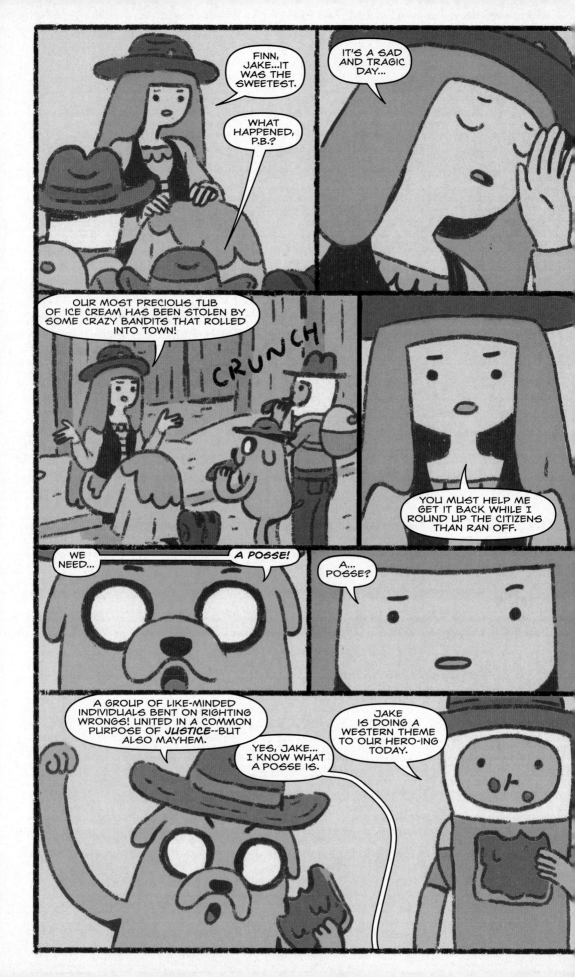

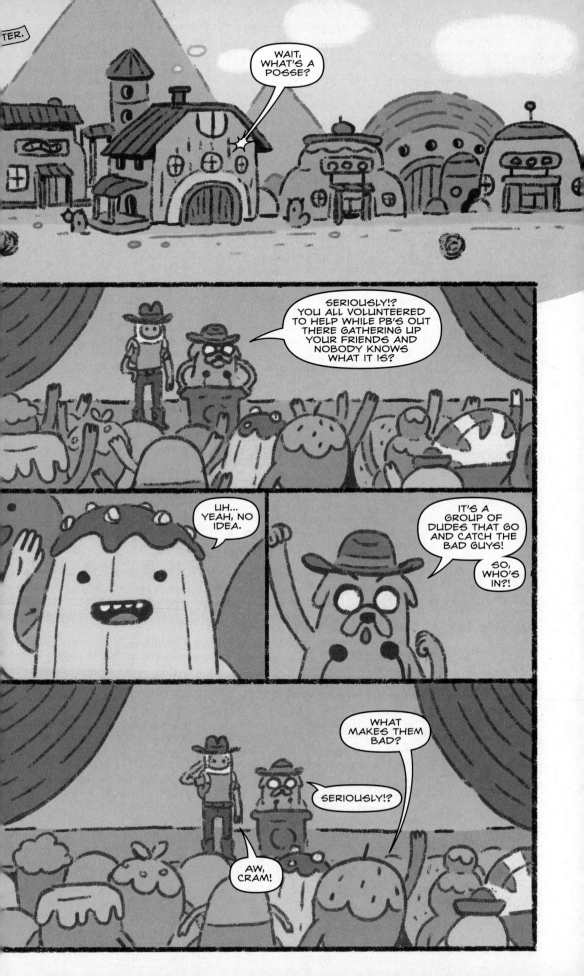

WE'RE GONNA NEED SOMEONE TO TRACK THOSE BANDITS, AND I KNOW THE BEST IN THE BIZ. THIS IS WHERE HE HANGS.
BAM
UH...JAKE, WHAT ARE YOU DOING?
SQUINTING.
SQUINTING INTO THE SALOON, PARTNER.
IT'S HOW YOU FIND PEOPLE IN SALOONS *DRAMATICALLY.*
AND IT WORKED-- THERE HE IS!

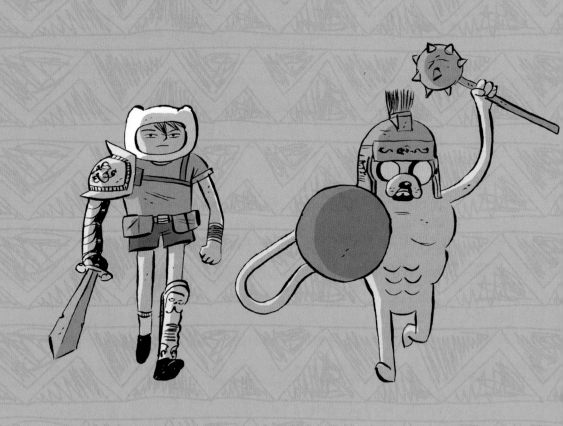

CANDY FINN

WRITTEN & ILLUSTRATED BY MORGAN BEEM
LETTERING BY WARREN MONTGOMERY

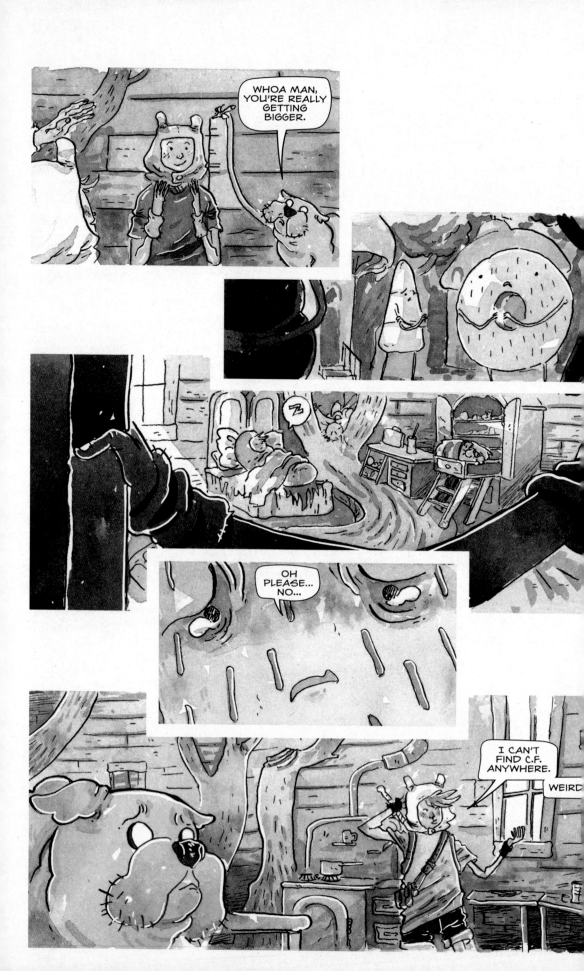

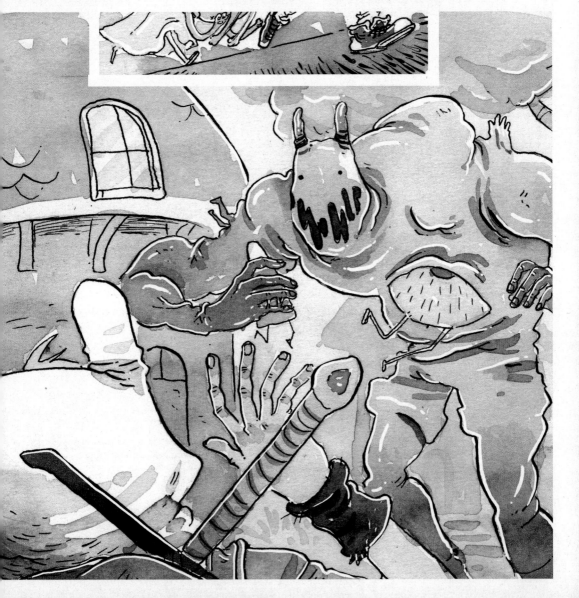

YOU'RE ALIVE!

JUST SHOWS THAT YOU NEED MORE THAN SPIT AND SUGAR TO BE AS COOL AS ME AND FINN.

ACTUALLY, IT WAS A MIXTURE OF--

YEP, MORE THAN SPIT. GOT IT.

THE END

Adventure Time

C'MON grab your friends

we're going to very distant lands

with Jake the Dog

and Finn the Human

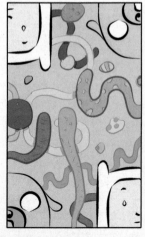

the fun

will never end, it's

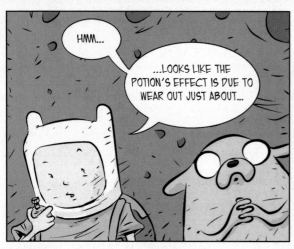

HMM...

...LOOKS LIKE THE POTION'S EFFECT IS DUE TO WEAR OUT JUST ABOUT...

NOW

CAN HARDLY SEE 'EM FROM UP HERE.

EH, DON'T LET THEIR SIZE FOOL YOU...

...THOSE MONSTERS MEAN BUSINESS!

WELL...TIME TO HEAD BACK TO THE TREE FORT, I GUESS.

WHAT?

WHAT? WE'LL GO BACK THE SAME WAY WE CAME...?

AH...ALL THAT MAGICKIN' AND FIGHTIN' TIRES A FELLOW OUT...

POP

SO...

SO, WE CAN TAKE THE BUS.

THE BUS?

FINN & JAKE IN

SHOULD WE STAY OR SHOULD WE GO

by Sonny Liew

2   7   17
21   30   64
112   135

HMMM...

WHICH ONE GOES TO THE GRASS LANDS OF OOO?

BEATS ME...

WE CAN JUST ASK THE DRIVER OF THE NEXT ONE THAT COMES ALONG.

COULD DO WITH A BITE TO EAT...

21 30 64
112 135

LET'S SEE...

WE'VE GOT CHOCOLATE BOMBS, CHEESE WINKLES AND A COUPLE OF GRAFFY BARS...

I'LL HAVE A WINKLE!

DO YOU KNOW WHAT TIME IT IS?

4:30

EXCELLENT! STILL TIME FOR SNACKS WITHOUT SPOILING DINNER THEN!

5:37 PM

A BUS AT *LAST!*

DO YOU GO BY THE GRASSLANDS OF OOO?

NAH...YOU'LL HAVE TO CATCH THE NO. 7 FOR THAT.

OK...

THANKS, MISTER!

HEY, IT'S MARCELINE!

HEY, JAKE. WASSUP, FINN.

WHAT ARE YOU DOING HERE?

I'VE GOT TO TRANSFER TO ANOTHER BUS TO GET TO WHERE I'M GOING...

YEAH, BUT, MARCY, YOU CAN *FLY* EVERYWHERE.

WELL...

SOMETIMES IT'S JUST NICE TO SIT ON THE BUS AND WATCH THE WORLD GO BY.

LEAN YOUR HEAD AGAINST THE GLASS AND NOT WORRY ABOUT WHERE OR HOW FAST YOU'RE GOING...

'SIDES, IT GIVES ME THE CHANCE TO CHILL OUT AND LISTEN TO SOME TUNES.

WOAAH

IT'S THE NEW ALBUM FROM THE *PERSISTENT FOODBRAINS*.

THEY'RE AN AGITATOR METAL BAND FROM THE EDGE OF THE NIGHTOSPHERE...

SONGS ABOUT LOVE AND HEARTBREAK, WITH SPLASHY CYMBALS , WALL-CLIMBING BASSLINES AND TORRENTIAL GUITARS.

AND THEIR LEAD SINGER FRANKIE MAKO PLAYS THE MEANEST TWIN MONOSYNTHS THIS SIDE OF SEVERAL PARALLELVERSES.

Should We Stay or Should We Go

by The Mathematicals

Should we stay or should we go

Neither seems to be particularly bad

Except that sometimes it's

Hurtful just the same

If we stayed it could be alright

A collision of planets in the inky dark

Some things lost

Other things found

Should we stay or should we go

I guess there are choices

Neither good nor bad

But sometimes

Hurtful all the same

SO WE HAVE TO FIGURE OUT WHAT MAKES ONE THING LIKE ANOTHER...

...WHICH SEEMS EASY ENOUGH WITH A FROG AND A TOAD, OR A RAT AND A MOUSE...

...BUT THEN A FLY HAS WINGS.

AND A BIRD HAS WINGS.

AND A UNICORN HAS NO WINGS, YET IT IS MORE LIKE A BIRD THAN A BIRD IS LIKE A FLY.

AND A LUMBERJACK MIGHT CALL ALL CONIFER TREES SOFTWOODS AND ALL BROAD LEAF TREES HARDWOODS...

...WHEN REALLY THERE ARE CONIFERS THAT EXIST WHOSE WOODS ARE MUCH HARDER THAN ANY HARDWOODS OUT THERE...

the bristly Bottle Imp.
An exceedingly rare species
on leaves & berries,

MUCH LATER.

WHERE IS THAT BUSSSSS??!!!

OH, WAIT, HERE IT COMES.

GOOD GLOB, YOU'RE HERE AT *LAST!*

WE'VE BEEN WAITING FOR THE NO.7 FOR *AAAAGESSS!*

SEVEN?

PARDON ME A MOMENT.

AH, ONE OF THE NUMBERS MUST'VE FALLEN OFF – WE'RE A *NO. 17* BUS, IN FACT.

HI FINN, HI JAKE.

BMO!

COVER GALLERY

MIKE HENDERSON

PIUS BAK

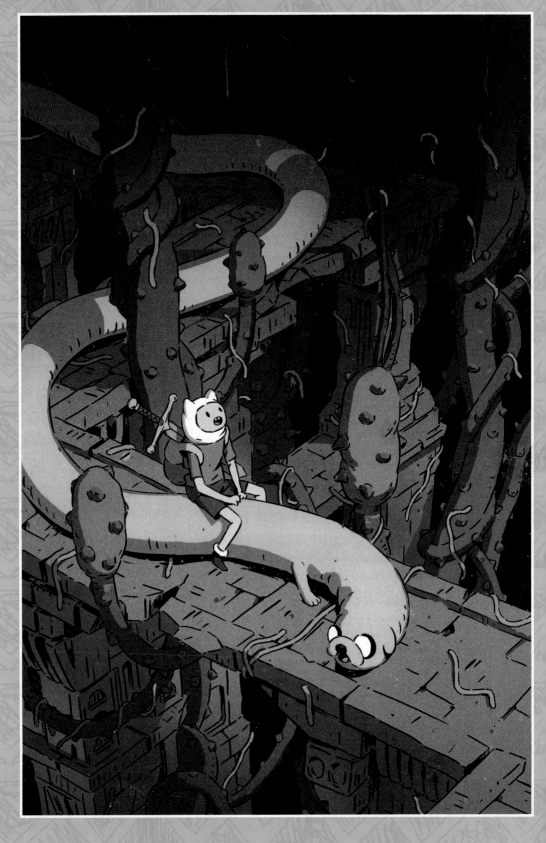

DISCOVER MORE
ADVENTURE TIME

Adventure Time

Volume 1
ISBN: 978-1-60886-280-1 | $14.99 US

Volume 2
ISBN: 978-1-60886-323-5 | $14.99 US

Volume 3
ISBN: 978-1-60886-317-4 | $14.99

Volume 4
ISBN: 978-1-60886-351-8 | $14.99

Volume 5
ISBN: 978-1-60886-401-0 | $14.99

Volume 6
ISBN: 978-1-60886-482-9 | $14.99

Volume 7
ISBN: 978-1-60886-746-2 | $14.99

Volume 8
ISBN: 978-1-60886-795-0 | $14.99

Volume 9
ISBN: 978-1-60886-843-8 | $14.99

Volume 10
ISBN: 978-1-60886-909-1 | $14.99

Volume 11
ISBN: 978-1-60886-946-6 | $14.99

Volume 12
ISBN: 978-1-68415-005-2 | $14.99

Volume 13
ISBN: 978-1-68415-051-9 | $14.99

Volume 14
ISBN: 978-1-68415-144-8 | $14.99

Volume 15
ISBN: 978-1-68415-203-2 | $14.99

Volume 16
ISBN: 978-1-68415-272-8 | $14.99

Adventure Time Comics

Volume 1
ISBN: 978-1-60886-934-3 | $14.99

Volume 2
ISBN: 978-1-60886-984-8 | $14.99

Volume 3
ISBN: 978-1-68415-041-0 | $14.99

Volume 4
ISBN: 978-1-68415-133-2 | $14.99

Volume 5
ISBN: 978-1-68415-190-5 | $14.99

Volume 6
ISBN: 978-1-68415-258-2 | $14.99

Adventure Time Original Graphic Novels

Volume 1 Playing With Fire
ISBN: 978-1-60886-832-2 | $14.99

Volume 2 Pixel Princesses
ISBN: 978-1-60886-329-7 | $11.99

Volume 3 Seeing Red
ISBN: 978-1-60886-356-3 | $11.99

Volume 4 Bitter Sweets
ISBN: 978-1-60886-430-0 | $12.99

Volume 5 Graybles Schmaybles
ISBN: 978-1-60886-484-3 | $12.99

Volume 6 Masked Mayhem
ISBN: 978-160886-764-6 | $14.99

Volume 7 The Four Castles
ISBN: 978-160886-797-4 | $14.99

Volume 8 President Bubblegum
ISBN: 978-1-60886-846-9 | $14.99

Volume 9 The Brain Robbers
ISBN: 978-1-60886-875-9 | $14.99

Volume 10 The Orient Express
ISBN: 978-1-60886-995-4 | $14.99

Volume 11 Princess & Princess
ISBN: 978-1-68415-025-0 | $14.99

Volume 12 Thunder Road
ISBN: 978-1-68415-179-0 | $14.99